First Print Edition [1.0] -1435 h. (2014 c.e.)

Copyright © 1435 H./2014 C.E.
Taalib al-Ilm Educational Resources

http://taalib.com
Learn Islaam, Live Islaam.^{SM}

ISBN EAN-13:   978-1-938117-20-6   [Soft cover Print Edition]

GOLDEN WORDS UPON GOLDEN WORDS...FOR EVERY MUSLIM.

"Imaam al-Barbahaaree, may Allaah have mercy upon him said:

May Allaah have mercy upon you! Examine carefully the speech of everyone you hear from in your time particularly. So do not act in haste and do not enter into anything from it until you ask and see: Did any of the Companions of the Prophet, may Allaah's praise and salutations be upon him, speak about it, or did any of the scholars? So if you find a narration from them about it, cling to it, do not go beyond it for anything and do not give precedence to anything over it and thus fall into the Fire.

Explanation by Sheikh Saaleh al-Fauzaan, may Allaah preserve him:

'Do not be hasty in accepting as correct what you may hear from the people especially in these later times. As now there are many who speak about so many various matters, issuing rulings and ascribing to themselves both knowledge and the right to speak. This is especially the case after the emergence and spread of new modern day media technologies. Such that everyone now can speak and bring forth that which is in truth worthless; by this meaning words of no true value - speaking about whatever they wish in the name of knowledge and in the name of the religion of Islaam. It has even reached the point that you find the people of misguidance and the members of the various groups of misguidance and deviance from the religion speaking as well. Such individuals have now become those who speak in the name of the religion of Islaam through means such as the various satellite television channels. Therefore be very cautious!

It is upon you oh Muslim, and upon you oh student of knowledge individually, to verify matters and not rush to embrace everything and anything you may hear. It is upon you to verify the truth of what you hear, asking, 'Who else also makes this same statement or claim?', 'Where did this thought or concept originate or come from?', 'Who is its reference or source authority?'. Asking what are the evidences which support it from within the Book and the Sunnah? And inquiring where has the individual who is putting this forth studied and taken his knowledge from? From who has he studied the knowledge of Islaam?

Each of these matters requires verification through inquiry and investigation, especially in the present age and time. As it is not every speaker who should rightly be considered a source of knowledge, even if he is well spoken and eloquent, and can manipulate words captivating his listeners. Do not be taken in and accept him until you are aware of the degree and scope of what he possesses of knowledge and understanding. As perhaps someone's words may be few, but possess true understanding, and perhaps another will have a great deal of speech yet he is actually ignorant to such a degree that he doesn't actually posses anything of true understanding. Rather he only has the ability to enchant with his speech so that the people are deceived. Yet he puts forth the perception that he is a scholar, that he is someone of true understanding and comprehension, that he is a capable thinker, and so forth. Through such means and ways he is able to deceive and beguile the people, taking them away from the way of truth.

Therefore what is to be given true consideration is not the amount of the speech put forth or that one can extensively discuss a subject. Rather the criterion that is to be given consideration is what that speech contains within it of sound authentic knowledge, what it contains of the established and transmitted principles of Islaam. As perhaps a short or brief statement which is connected to or has a foundation in the established principles can be of greater benefit than a great deal of speech which simply rambles on, and through hearing you don't actually receive very much benefit from.

This is the reality which is present in our time; one sees a tremendous amount of speech which only possesses within it a small amount of actual knowledge. We see the presence of many speakers yet few people of true understanding and comprehension.' "

[The eminent major scholar Sheikh Saaleh al-Fauzaan, may Allaah preserve him- 'A Valued Gift for the Reader Of Comments Upon the Book Sharh as-Sunnah', page 102-103]

❨ *Is not He better than your so-called gods, He Who originates creation and shall then repeat it, and Who provides for you from heaven and earth? Is there any god with Allaah? Say: 'Bring forth your proofs, if you are truthful.'* ❩-(Surah an-Naml: 64)

Explanation: ❨ **Say: "Bring forth your proofs.."** ❩ This is a command for the Prophet, may Allaah praise and salutation be upon him, to rebuke them immediately after they had put forward their own rebuke. Meaning: '*Say to them: bring your proof, whether it is an intellectual proof or a proof from transmitted knowledge, that would stand as evidence that there is another with Allaah, the Most Glorified and the Most Exalted*'. Additionally, it has been said that it means: '*Bring your proof that there is anyone other than Allaah, the Most High, who is capable of doing that which has been mentioned from His actions, the Most Glorified and the Most Exalted.*' ❨ **...if you are truthful.** ❩ meaning, in this claim. From this it is derived that a claim is not accepted unless clearly indicated by evidences."

[*Tafseer al-'Aloosee: vol. 15, page 14*]

Sheikh Rabee'a Ibn Hadee Umair al-Madkhalee, may Allaah preserve him said,

'It is possible for someone to simply say, "*So and so said such and such.*" However we should say, "*Produce your proof.*" So why did you not ask them for their proof by saying to them: "*Where was this said?*" Ask them questions such as this, as from your weapons are such questions as: "*Where is this from? From which book? From which cassette?...*" '

[*The Overwhelming Falsehoods of 'Abdul-Lateef Bashmeel' page 14*]

The guiding scholar Imaam Sheikh 'Abdul-'Azeez Ibn Abdullah Ibn Baaz, may Allaah have mercy upon him, said,

'It is not proper that any intelligent individual be mislead or deceived by the great numbers from among people from the various countries who engage in such a practice. As the truth is not determined by the numerous people who engage in a matter, rather the truth is known by the Sharee'ah evidences. Just as Allaah the Most High says in Surah al-Baqarah, ❨ **And they say, "None shall enter Paradise unless he be a Jew or a Christian." These are only their own desires. Say "Produce your proof if you are truthful."** ❩-(Surah al-Baqarah: 111) And Allaah the Most High says ❨ **And if you obey most of those on the earth, they will mislead you far away from Allaah's path. They follow nothing but conjectures, and they do nothing but lie.** ❩-(Surah al-'Ana'an: 116)'

[*Collection of Rulings and Various Statements of Sheikh Ibn Baaz -Vol. 1 page 85*]

Sheikh Muhammad Ibn 'Abdul-Wahaab, may Allaah have mercy upon him, said,

'Additionally verify that knowledge held regarding your beliefs, distinguishing between what is correct and false within it, coming to understand the various areas of knowledge of faith in Allaah alone and the required disbelief in all other objects of worship. You will certainly see various different matters which are called towards and enjoined; so if you see that a matter is in fact one coming from Allaah and His Messenger, then this is what is intended and is desired that you possess. Otherwise, Allaah has certainly given you that which enables you to distinguish between truth and falsehood, if Allaah so wills.

Moreover, this writing of mine- do not conceal it from the author of that work; rather present it to him. He may repent and affirm its truthfulness and then return to the guidance of Allaah, or perhaps if he says that he has a proof for his claims, even if that is only a single statement or if he claims that within my statements there is something unsupported, then request his evidence for that assertion. After this if there is something which continues to cause uncertainty or is a problem for you, then refer it back to me, so that then you are aware of both his statement and mine in that issue. We ask Allaah to guide us, you, and all the Muslims to that which He loves and is pleased with.'

[Personal Letters of Sheikh Muhammad Ibn 'Abdul-Wahaab- Conclusion to Letter 20]

Sheikh 'Abdullah Ibn 'Abdur-Rahman Abu Bateen, may Allaah have mercy upon him, said,

'And for an individual, if it becomes clear to him that something is the truth, he should not turn away from it and or be discouraged simply due to the few people who agree with him and the many who oppose him in that, especially in these latter days of this present age.

If the ignorant one says: *"If this was the truth so and so and so and so would have been aware of it!"* However this is the very claim of the disbelievers, in their statement found in the Qur'aan ⟨ **If it had truly been good, they would not have preceded us to it!"** ⟩-(Surah al-Ahqaaf: 11) and in their statement ⟨ **Is it these whom Allaah has favored from amongst us?"** ⟩-(Surah al-Ana'am: 53). Yet certainly as Alee Ibn Abee Taalib, may Allaah be pleased with him, stated *"Know the truth and then you will know it's people."* But for the one who generally stands upon confusion and uncertainty, then every doubt swirls around him. And if the majority of the people were in fact upon the truth today, then Islaam would not be considered strange, yet by Allaah it is today seen as the most strange of affairs!"

[Durar As-Sanneeyyah -vol. 10, page 400]

Table of Contents

How to use this Exercise Workbook

This workbook can be used to make it simpler for the one administering a study circle to check all lesson homework, quizzes and tests from the answer key which is available at the back of the [Self Study/Teachers Edition]. Exercise workbooks can be collected after class or at another convenient time for student work to be checked before proceeding to the next lesson.

A teacher marking area has been added for indicating correct and incorrect answers on the outside margin of each page. There is a [/] at the bottom of that marking area for recording the number of correct answers out of total answers written on that page.

NAME: _____

TEACHER:_____

START DATE: _____

END DATE: _____

LESSON ONE EXERCISES

Key Terms in this Lesson

Define these terms:

العقيدة:

In the language:

In the Islamic legislation:

الإيمان:

ثلاثة الأصول:

التوحيد:

Lesson Questions

Level 1: (required)

1. What are the two categories of *al-eemaan* according to the scholars?

2. What is the name of the book, in English and Arabic, which we are studying? Is this the only name by which this book is known? Explain.

3. What is the full name of the author of the book we are studying? Where was he born and when?

4. What is the subject of the book?

[/]

Level 2: (supplementary)

1. Some people say that the verse, ❪*There is no compulsion in religion*❫ means that we do not have to follow those commands of Allaah that are too difficult for us, or that we do not like. How would you explain the correct explanation of this verse to them?

2. What are some points of benefit that we can find in the life story of Sheik Muhammad ibn 'Abdul Wahaab? List two ways that you would like to take him as an example in your own life.

3. Why is it incorrect for people to call the ones who believe as Sheikh Muhammad ibn 'Abdul Wahaab believed, "Wahaabis"? What are they, in truth?

4. Why is this book a good one to be studied by the Muslims? Who are some of the scholars who have recommended it?

LESSON TWO EXERCISES
Key Terms in this Lesson

Define these terms:

البسملة:

لفظ الجلالة:

الله:

الرحمن:

الرحيم:

Lesson Questions:

Level 1: [required]

1. What two ahaadeeth are these three principles derived from?

2. What is the ruling on beginning a book with the *basmalah*?

[/]

3. What is the difference between the two names of Allaah, الرحمن and الرحيم؟

Level 2: [supplementary]

1. Why did the sheikh begin the book with the *basmalah*? What does it mean that there is an unspoken component to the *basmalah*?

2. Take a minute to look at yourself, and examine your purpose for studying this book. What do you hope to gain by it? What are some ways that you can, with the grace and mercy of Allaah succeed to attain your goals?

[/]

LESSON THREE EXERCISES
Key Terms in this Lesson

Define these terms:

المتن:

الرحمة:

العلم:

The definition of Sheikh 'Utheimeen and other than him, which is a general definition:

The definition of Ibn Qayyim and other than him, which is a specific definition:

The definition of Sheikh Muhammad ibn 'Abdul Wahaab and other than him:

الجهل:

الوهم:

الشك:

الظن:

ضروري:

نظري:

الدليل:

Lesson Questions

Level 1: (required)

1. What are two benefits of beginning the work with the command to "know"?

2. What are the six levels of comprehension given by Sheikh 'Utheimeen?

3. What is the Islamic ruling on seeking knowledge? Be specific in your answer.

4. What is textual proof? What is intellectual proof?

Level 2: (supplementary)

1. What are two things which are indicated by the Sheikh's supplication for Allaah's mercy upon the reader?

[/]

LESSON FOUR EXERCISES

Key Terms in this Lesson

Define these terms:

:الدعوة

:الصبر

Lesson Questions:

Level 1: (required)

1. What is the ruling on calling to Islaam? Explain how a person with little knowledge, if it is sound, can call to Islaam.

2. What are the categories of patience? List an example of each.

Level 2: (supplementary)

1. Explain the interconnectedness of knowledge with action.

[/]

2. List the five categories of action along with an example of each. How can you consciously raise the level of an action so that it becomes something you are rewarded for?

3. How could you advise someone who is upset with the decree of Allaah, who thinks that Allaah is not listening to him or helping him?

[/]

LESSON FIVE EXERCISES

Key Terms in this Lesson

Define these terms:

العصر:

جهاد النفس:

Lesson Questions:

Level 1: (required)

1. Is it permissible to swear by other than Allaah, as this is what Allaah does in the Qur'aan? Why or why not?

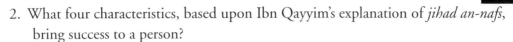

2. What four characteristics, based upon Ibn Qayyim's explanation of *jihad an-nafs*, bring success to a person?

3. Name two scholars mentioned in this section of the text and tell a little about them.

[/]

Level 2: (supplementary)

   1. How is it that Surat al-'Asr is a proof for the four matters mentioned? Where are these matters mentioned in the Surah?

   2. Does the saying of ash-Shafi'ee, may Allaah have mercy upon him, mean that a Muslim simply needs to know Surat al-'Asr and nothing else concerning the religion? Explain.

3. Explain the position of knowledge in relation to speech and action.

4. What are some of the dangers of speaking without knowledge?

[/]

LESSON SIX EXERCISES
Key Terms in this Lesson

Define these terms:

توحيد الربوبية

توحيد الألوهية:

الولاء:

البراء:

الرزق:

Lesson Questions:

Level 1: (required)

1. What three matters are discussed in this section, as clarified by Sheikh Fauzaan, may Allaah preserve him?

2. How would you prove to someone that Allaah created everything?

[/]

3. Explain the two types of *ar-rizq*.

4. How did Sheikh al-Islaam ibn Taimiyyah, may Allaah have mercy upon him, categorize the commands of Allaah? Give an example of each.

Level 2: (supplementary)

1. What proof is there that we have a purpose in life? What is that purpose?

2. Explain the position of the intellect in Islaam.

3. How can one refuse to enter Paradise? Explain.

4. Why is the fact that Allaah sent messengers and prophets to the mankind and jinn a manifestation of His, Glorified is He, Most High, mercy?

[/]

LESSON SEVEN EXERCISES
Key Terms in this Lesson

Define these terms

دعاء مسألة :

دعاء عبادة :

المسجد / المساجد :

:الموالاة

Lesson Questions:

Level 1: (required)

1. What are the two types of *du'a*? Explain them and give an example of each.

2. What are the ten ways which Sheikh Fauzaan lists to show *al-baraa'* from the disbelievers?

[/]

3. What are the two categories of disbelievers? What are the differences between them?

Level 2: (supplementary)

1. What is the meaning of *tawheed al-uloohiyyah?* Why is it so crucial that we understand it and live by it?

2. Explain *al-walaa'* and *al-baraa*, and how we can put them into action in our everyday lives.

3. Is it permissible to harm or kill people just because they are disbelievers? Explain.

[/]

LESSON EIGHT EXERCISES

Key Terms in this Lesson

Define these terms:

الرشد:

الطاعة:

العبادة:

The general meaning:

The specific meaning:

التوحيد:

الشرك:

Lesson Questions:

Level 1: (required)

1. What is الحنيفية ؟ Who is Ibraaheem?

2. What is الإخلاص؟

3. What are the four categories of major shirk? Briefly describe them.

[/]

4. What is the lesser shirk? Give an example of this.

Level 2: (supplementary)

1. What are some of the fruits of having الإخلاص؟

2. Explain the two types of *al-ibaadah*, and give an example of each.

3. Sheikh Fauzaan, may Allaah preserve him, says that *tawheed* is from the meaning of *'ibaadah*. Explain how this is true.

4. Is this statement true or false: We must stay completely away from major *shirk*, but minor *shirk* is not such a big deal- it doesn't take us out of the religion or anything. Explain your answer.

[/]

QUIZ NUMBER ONE

THIS QUIZ COVERS LESSONS ONE THROUGH EIGHT.

Use a separate piece of paper for this quiz. It must be torn out of the notebook. Write your full name and kunya in the upper left hand corner. Write each term to be defined before its definition, and number each answer to the questions clearly. Write neatly, as if the answer cannot be read, it will count as wrong.

Define these terms:

العقيدة:

In the Islamic legislation:

التوحيد:

الإيمان:

ثلاثة الأصول:

العلم:

الدليل:

جهاد النفس:

توحيد الربوبية:

[/]

توحيد الألوهية:

الطاعة:

العبادة: (both the general meaning and the specific meaning)

الولاء:

البراء:

Questions:

1. What are the two types of *al-eeman* or faith? Describe each one briefly, and provide one example of each.

2. Who is the author of *"Thalaathatul-Usool?* Give a brief biography of him.

3. What is the ruling of beginning a book with the basmalah? What example does this follow?

4. What is the Islamic ruling on seeking knowledge? Be as specific as possible in your answer.

[/]

5. Explain the difference between textual proof and intellectual proof? Which one is taken first and foremost in matters of the religion?

6. What are the categories of patience? List an example of each.

7. What is the difference between *fard ʿayn* and *fard kifaayyah*? Give an example of each.

8. What four characteristics, based upon Ibn Qayyim's explanation of *jihad an-nafs*, bring success to a person?

9. Explain the position of knowledge in relation to speech and action.

10. What are the two types of *du'a*? Explain them and give an example of each.

11. List five ways that we can show *al-baraa'* from the disbelievers.

12. List five ways that we can show *al-walaa'* for the Believers.

[/]

13. What is الإخلاص al-ikhlaas?

14. What is الشرك ash-shirk? For extra points, list the different types of shirk and give an example of each.

15. Take a few minutes to write down some of the benefits that you have gained from this course so far- what are some specific ways that you can make your *'aqeedah* a part of your life? For example, what are some ways that you can give *da'wah* right now? List at least two specific goals for yourself to begin working towards today.

[/]

LESSON NINE EXERCISES

Key Terms in this Lesson

Define these terms:

أصل/ الأصول:

التربية:

الحمد:

العالم/ العالمين:

Lesson Questions:

Level 1: (required)

1. Why is it obligatory that every Muslim have knowledge of these three matters mentioned in the lesson?

2. What are some types of *at-tarbiyyah* and what, according to Sheikh Saalih aal-Sheikh, is the greatest of the categories of *at-tarbiyyah*?

3. How are *tawheed ar-ruboobiyyah* and *tawheed al-uloohiyyah* intertwined and connected?

4. Explain the term *al-ʿaalameen,* and give some examples of what is included in this term.

[/]

Level 2: (supplementary)

1. Using the explanation of Sheikh 'Abdur Rahman ibn Qaasim an-Najdee, briefly discuss what these three matters are and what they entail.

2. How is it that some individuals and groups do not recognize that which is most important, but rather focus on matters that are not as important? What is wrong with this?

3. How can inner acts of submission to Allaah lead to outer acts of submission?

4. What are two proofs that all praise is due to Allaah, alone?

[/]

LESSON TEN EXERCISES

Key Terms in this Lesson

Define these terms:

آية/ الآيات:

Lesson Questions:

Level 1: (required)

1. What are the two types of *ayaat*? List two examples of each.

2. What are the two types of commandment? Give two examples of your own which are not mentioned in the text.

3. Why is it not possible for us to compare Allaah to His creation?

4. How do the two verses from Surat al-Baqarah (21-22) both affirm that we must worship Allaah alone, and negate associating others along with Him in worship?

5. Who is Ibn Katheer and what are two of his most famous works?

[/]

Level 2: (supplementary)

1. How can revelation teach us about Allaah?

2. How can looking at the signs of Allaah in creation teach us about Allaah?

3. What is one way you could respond to someone who says he worships nature, or the sun, or some other inanimate object?

4. Take time out to sit down with your journal or notebook and write down as many of the blessings of Allaah that you can think of. Make sure you write down the ones that you often may take for granted. When you are finished, look at the list and thank Allaah for all of those blessings as well as all of those which you did not list, and make a commitment to thank Him at least every day for all that He has given to you. Lastly, look at them and try to understand what they tell you about Allaah from those names and attributes of His which you know are confirmed in the Qur'aan and Sunnah. For example, in the way that you see your wife nurse your baby, you can see Allaah's mercy and wisdom, among other things.

[/]

LESSON ELEVEN EXERCISES
Key Terms in this Lesson

Define these terms:

العبادة:

النية:

القصد:

المسجد/ المساجد:

الدعاء:

مشرك:

كافر :

Lesson Questions:

Level 1: (required)

1. What are the two divisions of worship, and how can these be both apparent and hidden? If desired, make a chart or diagram to show this more clearly.

2. What category of *shirk* is being referred to in the text, describing one who directs worship to other than Allaah? What are some examples of directing acts of worship to other than Allaah? Give an example of speech, action, hidden and apparent.

3. How does one know if it is permissible to call upon or ask someone from the creation to assist them in something?

Level 2: (supplementary)

1. Explain in your own words why the definition of al-ʿibaadah by Sheikh al-Islaam ibn Taymiyyah, may Allaah have mercy upon him, is comprehensive, and how it can help us change our lives for the better?

*
[/]

2. Explain how this verse provides evidence that one cannot direct any act of worship to other than Allaah, alone: *"Indeed the places of worship (masaajid) are for Allaah alone, so invoke not anyone along with Allaah."* *(Surat al-Jinn, Ayat 18)*

3. Give some examples of times when it is permissible to call on someone from the creation to assist you. Give some examples of when it is not permissible to do so.

[/]

LESSON TWELVE EXERCISES

Key Terms in this Lesson

Define these terms:

الخوف:

الرجاء:

التوكل:

الرغبة:

الرهبة:

الخشوع:

الخشية:

Lesson Questions:

Level 1: (required)

1. What are the three types of reverential fear (*al-khawf*)? Give an example of each.

2. What are the categories of *ar-rajaa*? Give an example of each.

[/]

3. Explain the differences between *al-khawf*, al-khashiyah, and *al-khushoo'*.

Level 2: (supplementary)

1. A family has a baby, which is born with a treatable heart defect. The parents refuse to have the baby treated, saying that they will rely upon Allaah and whatever happens was willed to happen. What is your response to this? How would you advise them?

2. Explain how *ar-raghbah* and *ar-rahbah* should be made a reality in the lives of the Believers.

[/]

LESSON THIRTEEN EXERCISES

Key Terms in this Lesson

Define these terms:

الإنابة:

الإستعانة:

الإستعاذة:

الإستغاثة:

الذبح:

النذر:

Lesson Questions:

Level 1: (required)

1. What are the two categories of *al-inaabah*? Which is general, and which is for the Believers only?

2. What are the categories of *al-isti'aanah*? Which are permissible, and which are forbidden?

[/]

3. Is it permissible to seek refuge through Allaah's names, attributes, words, and other than this? If so, give an example of this.

4. What are the three categories of sacrifice?

Level 2: (supplementary)

1. What are the four matters which must be present for one to be a *muneeb*, one who turns to Allaah in repentance?

2. How is it that *al-isti'aanah* to Allaah is the perfection of submission of the worshipper to His Lord, and how does in include the saying, "There is no power nor strength except with Allaah"?

[/]

3. A person is walking home on a dark night, and falls into a dark, deep hole. Is it permissible for him to call out for assistance, or should he just ask Allaah to deliver him from his predicament? Explain.

4. Why is it that the definition of *an-nadhr* includes that the person be of sound mind and mature age? Does this mean that it is alright for us to allow our children to say, "Wa Allaahi" about every little thing, as is the custom of many of the people today?

[/]

LESSON FOURTEEN EXERCISES

Key Terms in this Lesson

Define these terms:

الإسلام:

الإيمان:

التقليد:

البراء:

The general meaning:

The meaning in the Islamic legislation:

Lesson Questions:

Level 1: (required)

1. Explain the difference in the meaning of the words Islaam and *eemaan* when they are used separately and together.

2. What are the two categories of *al-baraa*?

[/]

3. What are the three categories of people in regards to *al-walaa'* and *al-baraa*?

4. What are the three levels of disassociation? When are they appropriate? Give an example of each.

Level 2: (supplementary)

1. How does submission include the actions of the heart, tongue, and limbs?

2. Why does obedience here include obeying both Allaah and His Messenger?

[/]

3. You move to a Muslim country, and your neighbor comes over to visit you. In the course of the discussion you see that, while he believes in Allaah, and that Muhammad is His Messenger and other tenets of the faith, he has no idea what the proofs for these things are. In essence, he is a blind follower. Is he a Muslim, or not? Explain your answer.

4. List five of the ways Sheikh Saalih Fauzaan, may Allaah preserve him, tells us to show love and association for the Believers. Choose ones that you would like to immediately implement in your own life. Give practical examples of each.

[/]

QUIZ NUMBER TWO
THIS QUIZ COVERS LESSONS NINE THROUGH THIRTEEN

Use a separate piece of paper for this quiz. It must be torn out of the notebook. Write your full name and kunya in the upper left hand corner. Write each term to be defined before its definition, and number each answer to the questions clearly. Write neatly, as if the answer cannot be read, it will count as wrong.

1. Define these terms:

أصل/ الأصول:

التربية:

آية/ الآيات:

العبادة:

النية:

الدعاء:

مشرك:

كافر:

الخوف:

[/]

الرجاء:

التوكل:

الرغبة:

الرهبة:

الخشوع:

الخشية:

الإنابة:

الإستعانة:

الإستعاذة:

الإستغاثة:

[/]

الذبح:

النذر:

Questions:

1. Sheikh Muhammad ibn 'Abdul Wahaab, may Allaah have mercy upon him, states that it is obligatory upon every Muslim to *"...have knowledge of his Lord, his religion, and his Prophet, Muhammad, may Allaah's praise and salutations be upon him."* How are these three things foundations (*usool*) upon which the religion is built?

2. What is the most important thing that a Muslim must focus on in order to be successful in this life and the next? Why must he avoid being drawn too deeply into side issues?

3. What are some of the categories of *at-tarbiyyah*? What is said to be the greatest category of *tarbiyyah* which Allaah has bestowed upon mankind?

4. What aspect of *at-tawheed* does the Sheikh's saying, *He is the One whom I worship, and there is none other whom I worship other than Him* directly refer to?

5. What are the two categories of *ayaat,* or signs, by which we can learn about Allaah? Briefly explain them.

6. What are the two categories of Allaah's commands? Briefly describe them.

[/]

7. Give an example of worship in speech, worship in action, worship which is an act of the heart, worship which is hidden, and worship which is apparent.

8. "As long as we worship Allaah, we are okay." "Yes, we worship Allaah, we just visit the graves of our saints to honor them." Are these statements correct? Explain your answer.

9. What are the conditions by which it is permissible to seek something from other than Allaah?

10. What are the three categories of fear (*al-khawf*)? Briefly explain each one, with examples.

11. Is it acceptable that a person is consistently and constantly committing sins, hoping for Allaah's mercy? Explain.

[/]

12. What two things must be combined in *at-tawakkul* for it to be correct?

13. What are the two types of *al-inaabah*? Briefly explain each.

What is the meaning of the saying, "There is no power (to change) nor strength except with Allaah"- *la hawla wa la quwatta ila billaah*- (لا حول ولا قوة إلا بالله)? How does it relate to appealing to Allaah for assistance (*al-isti'aanah*)?

14. What are the three types of sacrifice *(adh-dhabh)?*

15. What are the conditions of making *al-isti'aanah*, *al-isti'aadhah*, and *al-istighathah* to other than Allaah without it being considered *shirk*? Give an example of one of these.

16. Give an example of a permissible vow. Give an example of one which is forbidden

[/]

LESSON FIFETEEN EXERCISES

Key Terms in this Lesson

Define these terms:

ركن/ الأركان :

البدعة :

In the language:

In the Islamic Legislation:

Lesson Questions:

Level 1: (required)

1. Many books translate the first part of the *shahaadah* as "I testify that there is no god but Allaah..." Why is this an incorrect interpretation and translation?

2. What are the four matters contained in testifying that Muhammad is the Messenger of Allaah?

3. What are the boundaries for innovation mentioned in the lesson?

[/]

4. List the two different categories of innovation, as well as the classifications of the second category. Give an example of each one that is not mentioned in the text.

Level 2: (supplementary)

1. Why is it stated that the five matters mentioned are pillars of Islaam, as opposed to just being parts that make up the whole of Islaam? What differentiates them from other legislated acts in this regard?

2. Why must the *shahaadah* include statement of the tongue, belief of the heart, and action of the limbs?

3. Why must we be very careful when dealing with the people of innovation?

[/]

LESSON SIXTEEN EXERCISES

Key Terms in this Lesson

Define these terms:

شرط/ شروط:

الصلاة:

الزكاة:

الصيام:

الحج:

Lesson Questions:

Level 1: (required)

1. Write the Arabic and English words for each of the conditions of the *shahaadah*. If you have studied the *Waajibaat*, insh'Allaah take some time to review the information there concerning these vital conditions.

2. Why does Allaah mention prayer and *zakaat* together in so many verses of Qur'aan, including "***and perform the prayers and give obligatory charity; and that is the right religion.***"?

[/]

3. List three benefits of the prayer as mentioned by Sheikh 'Abdullaah Fauzaan.

4. List three benefits of az-zakaat as mentioned by Sheikh 'Abdullaah Fauzaan

5. List five benefits of fasting as listed by Sheikh 'Abdullah Fauzaan.

[/]

Level 2: (supplementary)

1. Why is it crucial that a student of knowledge have a clear understanding of the *shahaadataan* in his heart and mind?

2. How can our faith increase if we understand and strive to realize all of the conditions of *ash-shahaadah*?

3. If a person is unable to afford going on *hajj*, is he a disbeliever?

4. What are some ways that you can see that the pillars of Islaam hold up not only the Islaam of the individual, but also the Islaam of the society?

[/]

LESSON SEVENTEEN EXERCISES

Key Terms in this Lesson

Define these terms:

الإيمان:

الركن/ أركان:

تحريف:

تعتيل:

تكييف:

تمثيل:

Lesson Questions:

Level 1: (required)

1. How does the hadeeth of the seventy and some branches of *eemaan* show that *eemaan* in its more general sense is not complete without action of the heart, tongue, and limbs?

2. How do we reconcile between the pillars of *eemaan* being only six, while the branches of *eemaan* are more than seventy?

[/]

3. What four matters are contained in belief or faith in Allaah?

4. What causes the people to turn away from the belief in Allaah's Lordship? Give an example from the Qur'aan.

5. What are some of the fruits of belief and faith in Allaah, alone?

[/]

Level 2: (supplementary)

1. You are teaching in a *masjid*, and mention that *eemaan* is made up of belief in the heart as well as action of the tongue and limbs. One of the students stands up and says that the only thing that is important is belief- as long as one believes, then his *eemaan* is correct. How would you reply to this person?

2. Briefly describe the four types of proof used to give evidence of Allaah's existence.

[/]

3. There are other gods that are worshipped besides Allaah alone. What are some of the proofs that this is a false and useless action?

4. What is the problem with each of the following statements:

a. Allaah loves His creation like a mother loves her baby

b. Allaah rose over His throne quickly

c. We can't say anything about Allaah's names and attributes at all!

d. The Qur'aan says that Allaah has a hand, but what it is referring to is Allaah's power.

[/]

LESSON EIGHTEEN EXERCISES

Key Terms in this Lesson

Define these terms:

ملك/ الملائكة:

كتاب/ كتب:

رسول/ رسل:

Lesson Questions:

Level 1: (required)

1. What four matters are encompassed in belief of the angels?

2. List the names of the Books we know have been sent down, as well as the messengers they were revealed to. Are these all the books there are?

3. Who was the first of the Messengers? Who was the last of them? Which five of them are known as the ones firmest in their resolve?

4. List the matters encompassed in the belief of the Books, and the belief in the messengers. Note how they are similar.

[/]

Level 2: (supplementary)

1. Some people claim that angels are not actual, created beings; rather they are metaphorical for the good in human beings or other such strange sayings. What is your reply to this false claim?

2. Is it permissible for us to act upon a ruling from the Tawrat or Injeel instead of that which is found in the Qur'aan, since they are all Allaah's Books? Why or why not?

3. There is no nation which was not sent either a messenger with prescribed laws, or a prophet to revive the laws of a previous messenger. How does this show the great mercy of Allaah?

4. A person says, "The messengers weren't anything special; they were men just like the rest of us." Is this true or false? Why?

[/]

LESSON NINETEEN EXERCISES
Key Terms in this Lesson

Define these terms:

اليوم الآخر:

الجنة:

النار:

القدر:

Lesson Questions:

Level 1: (required)

1. What is the resurrection? When will it occur?

2. Bring three textual proofs of the accounting and retribution. Why is it simply logical that it must occur?

3. What are the first two matters involved in belief in *al-qadr*? Bring one proof from the Qur'aan and one from the Sunnah to prove them.

Level 2: (supplementary)

1. Contrast *al-Jannah* and *an-Naar*. If possible, use verses and ahaadeeth from outside sources which describe these two places.

2. How can belief in the four matters encompassed in *al-qadr* allow us to grow in both patience and in gratitude?

3. How could you refute a person who claims that he is not responsible for performing obligatory acts, nor is he responsible for committing sins, because Allaah willed it to happen?

4. Sheikh 'Utheimeen says, "… in a person's worldly affairs he strives to take care of that which is in his best interests, seeking to attain it- and he does not, instead, strive to attain that which is not in his best interest and excuse himself in this with pre-decree. So why then does he turn away from that which benefits him in his religion, and instead does that which will harm him, and then use pre-decree as an excuse?" Bring an example of this.

[/]

LESSON TWENTY EXERCISES

Key Terms in this Lesson

Define these terms:

الإحسان:

الساعة:

القيامة:

Lesson Questions:

Level 1: (required)

1. What is meant by the definition of *ihsaan* given in the text- to worship Allaah as if you see Him, and if you do not see Him then know with certainty that He sees you?

2. What are the two categories of the religious meaning of *al-ihsaan*?

3. What were some of the characteristics or actions of the questioner in the hadeeth that amazed the Companions?

4. Why didn't the Prophet, may Allaah's praise and salutations be upon him, answer the question of when the Hour would be established?

[/]

Level 2: (supplementary)

1. List the three aspects of *ihsaan* towards the worshippers of Allaah, and bring an example of each.

2. Why might the Hadeeth of Jibraa'eel be called the mother of the Sunnah?

3. We know that some of the signs of the Hour have already occurred- does this mean that the Hour is close at hand?

4. What are some of the things that you, personally, have learned from the Hadeeth of Jibraa'eel? Are these things that you can implement in your own life? How?

[/]

QUIZ NUMBER THREE

THIS QUIZ COVERS LESSONS FOURTEEN THROUGH TWENTY.

Use a separate piece of paper for this quiz. It must be torn out of the notebook. Write your full name and kunya in the upper left hand corner. Write each term to be defined before its definition, and number each answer to the questions clearly. Write neatly, as if the answer cannot be read, it will count as wrong.

1. Define these terms:

الإسلام:

الإيمان: (the complete definition)

ركن/ الأركان:

البدعة:

شرط/ شروط:

الصلاة:

الزكاة:

الصيام:

الحج:

ملك/ الملائكة:

كتلب/ كتب :

رسول/ رسل:

القدر:

الإحسان:

Questions:

1. Explain the difference in the meaning of the words Islaam and *eemaan* when they are used separately and together.

2. How does submission include the actions of the heart, tongue, and limbs?

3. Why must we obey both Allaah and the Messenger of Allaah, may Allaah's praise and salutations be upon him?

4. Is it permissible to blindly follow others in matters related to *al-'aqeedah*? Explain.

5. What are the four matters contained in testifying that Muhammad is the Messenger of Allaah?

[/]

6. What are the two categories of innovation? Give examples of each. . For extra credit, list the different classifications of the second type of innovation.

7. Write the Arabic and English words for each of the conditions of the *shahaadah*.

8. What are some of the fruits of the prayer? How can establishing the prayer, being consistent in it, and striving to perfect it assist us in our everyday life?

9. What is the wisdom behind the fast? What are some of its benefits?

10. The Messenger of Allaah, may Allaah's praise and salutations be upon him, said, *al-eemaan is comprised of seventy and some branches...}*. Explain how *eemaan* can be compared to a tree, and what are its highest, middle, and lowest branches?

11. What are the four matters encompassed in belief in Allaah?

12. What are four ways in which some people go astray concerning Allaah's names and attributes? Give an example of each.

13. We must believe in and affirm all of the Books and the Messengers that Allaah has sent to mankind. Does this mean that we follow all of them? Explain.

14. What are some of the fruits of knowledge of the angels?

15. What three matters are encompassed by belief in the Last Day? What are some of the fruits of this belief?

[/]

16. Allaah has pre-decreed all things. Does this mean that we don't have to strive to please Him, or do all that we can to avoid displeasing Him, since our reward or punishment has already been written? Are we not responsible for our actions because Allaah has decreed that we do them?

17. What are the two categories of *al-ihsaan?* Give examples for each.

18. Write five points of benefit to be found in the hadeeth of Jibraa'eel.

[/]

LESSON TWENTY ONE EXERCISES

Key Terms in this Lesson

Define these terms:

محمد:

المعراج:

الإسراء:

Lesson Questions:

Level 1: (required)

1. Why is it crucial that we have knowledge of the Messenger of Allaah, may Allaah's praise and salutations be upon him?

2. What are some of the names of the Messenger of Allaah? What is the most famous one, as presented by the Sheikh in this work?

3. At what age did prophethood come to the Messenger of Allaah? How long did he live in Makkah? How long in Madinah? How old was he when he died?

4. What were the five stages of the Prophet's da'wah, as mentioned by Ibn Qayyim?

[/]

5. What basic message was the Prophet, may Allaah's praise and salutations be upon him, sent with?

Level 2: (supplementary)

1. Many of us have embraced Islaam after being brought up in or learning from another religious tradition such as Christianity. In both religions, we learn about the prophets such as Ibraaheem, Daawud, Yoonus, and others. Should we, then simply rely on the stories we learned in Christianity about these prophets and messengers? Why or why not?

2. With what did the Messenger of Allaah become a prophet? With what did he become a messenger? What is the difference between a prophet and a messenger?

3. What are the *israa'* and the *mi'raaj*? If you are able , write out the entire hadeeth concerning this as found in "*Saheeh al-Bukhaari*".

4. Using "*Saheeh al-Bukhaari*" and "*Saheeh Muslim*," write down ten hadeeth about the Prophet, may Allaah's praise and salutations be upon him. Take note of his noble characteristics in each one, and dedicate yourself to emulating him in these things.

[/]

LESSON TWENTY TWO EXERCISES

Key Terms in this Lesson

Define these terms:

الهجرة:

Its linguistic meaning:

Its meaning in the Islamic legislation:

Lesson Questions:

Level 1: (required)

1. What are the two main categories of *hijrah*?

2. What are the five types of physical *hijrah*? What are their general rulings?

3. Who is Imaam al-Baghawee?

4. Explain the hadeeth {*There is no hijrah after the opening (of Makkah), but fighting in the way of Allaah and the intention remain.*} in the context of the other hadeeth mentioned in the text which states that the *hijrah* will remain until the sun rises from its place of setting.

[/]

Level 2: (supplementary)

1. What is the general ruling on making *hijrah* from the land of disbelief to the land of Islaam? What is one of the reasons for this, as mentioned in the text of the lesson?

2. Why is the migration of the heart the foundation for *hijrah*? Why must this take place for the physical *hijrah* to follow?

3. Who are some of the people who will be forgiven for not making *hijrah* when it was obligatory upon them to do so? What is the proof of this?

[/]

LESSON TWENTY THREE EXERCISES

Key Terms in this Lesson

Define these terms:

المعروف:

المنكر:

Lesson Questions:

Level 1: (required)

1. Tell about the Prophet's, may Allaah's praise and salutations be upon him, death-where did he die, how did he die, how old was he, and what are some of the circumstances surrounding his death. Why is it so important that we understand and believe that he did, indeed, die?

2. What are some proofs from the Qur'aan and Sunnah that Allaah's Messenger, may Allaah's praise and salutations be upon him, was sent for all of mankind, and that we must follow him?

3. Why would it be impossible for us to only follow the Qur'aan, without the Sunnah?

[/]

Level 2: (supplementary)

1. Why was it a mercy to the Believers that most of the obligatory actions were not commanded until the Prophet, may Allaah's praise and salutations be upon him, was in al-Madina?

2. Why was commanding the good and forbidding the evil mentioned specifically by Sheikh Muhammad ibn 'Abdul Wahaab?

3. How would you respond to someone who says that it is perfectly fine to leave off some of the legislated acts of Islaam, because times have changed, and those things are no longer necessary?

[/]

LESSON TWENTY FOUR EXERCISES

Key Terms in this Lesson

Define these terms:

البعث: Its linguistic meaning:

Its meaning in the Islamic legislation:

العرض:

الحساب: The linguistic meaning:

Its meaning in the Islamic Legislation:

Lesson Questions:

Level 1: (required)

1. List some of the proofs for the Resurrection besides the verses mentioned in the text.

2. What takes place with each blowing of the trumpet on the Day of Resurrection?

3. What are some of the proofs that one who denies the Resurrection is a disbeliever?

[/]

Level 2: (supplementary)

1. What order will events take place in, on the Day of Resurrection?

2. What are the two categories of reckoning, and who falls under each one?

3. Why were messengers sent to mankind? List as many of them as you can think of.

[/]

LESSON TWENTY FIVE EXERCISES

Key Terms in this Lesson

Define these terms:

الطاغوت:

Its linguistic meaning:

Its meaning in the religion:

الغيب:

Lesson Questions:

Level 1: (required)

1. Were there any prophets or messengers before Nuh? Explain your answer.

2. What are the three types of *taaghoot*? Give examples of each.

3. What are the three ways in which we can disbelieve in the *taaghoot*? What are their rulings?

4. Who is Iblees? Why is he considered a head of the *taaghoot*?

5. What is the explanation of the verse, ❖ *There is no compulsion in religion. Verily, the Right Path has become distinct from the wrong path. Whoever disbelieves in taaghoot and believes in Allaah, then he has grasped the most trustworthy handhold that will never break.* ❖

[/]

Level 2: (supplementary)

1. Eesa, upon him be Allaah's praise, is worshipped by the Christians. Is he, therefore, a *taaghoot*? Explain your answer.

2. How can a scholar become a *taaghoot*?

3. What is the difference between the second and third heads of the *taaghoot* mentioned?

4. Why is one who claims knowledge of the unseen considered a head of the *taaghoot*?

5. True or false: Whoever judges by other than Allaah is a disbeliever. Explain your answer.

[/]

QUIZ NUMBER FOUR

THIS QUIZ COVERS LESSONS TWENTY-ONE THROUGH TWENTY-FIVE

Use a separate piece of paper for this quiz. It must be torn out of the notebook. Write your full name and kunya in the upper left hand corner. Write each term to be defined before its definition, and number each answer to the questions clearly. Write neatly, as if the answer cannot be read, it will count as wrong.

1. Define these terms:

    محمد:

    المعراج: Its linguistic meaning:

    Its meaning in the Islamic legislation:

    الإسراء: Its linguistic meaning:

Its meaning in the Islamic legislation:

الهجرة: Its linguistic meaning:

Its meaning in the Islamic legislation:

المعروف:

المنكر:

[/]

البعث: Its linguistic meaning:

Its meaning in the Islamic Legislation:

الحساب: The linguistic meaning:

Its meaning in the Islamic Legislation:

الطاغوت: Its linguistic meaning:

Its meaning in the religion:

الغيب:

Questions:

1. Who was the Prophet Muhammad, may Allaah's praise and salutations be upon him? Include his name, lineage, where he was born, where he died, at what age he received prophethood, how long his prophethood extended and at what age he died.

2. Why is it important that we know about the Messenger of Allaah, may Allaah's praise and salutations be upon him?

3. How did the Messenger of Allaah receive the prophethood? With what did he become a messenger? What was the message he was charged with spreading?

[/]

4. What were the five stages of the Prophet's *da'wah*, as mentioned by Ibn Qayyim?

5. What are the two main categories of *hijrah*?

6. What is the ruling on making *hijrah* from the land of disbelief to the land of Islaam, and what condition is placed upon that?

[/]

7. How would you reply to someone who says there isn't any *hijrah* at this time, due to the hadeeth, {*There is no hijrah after the opening (of Makkah), but fighting in the way of Allaah and the intention remain.*}?

8. Why is the migration of the heart the foundation for *hijrah*? Why must this take place for the physical *hijrah* to follow?

9. Why must we follow the Sunnah of the Messenger of Allaah?

[/]

10. What order will events take place in, on the Day of Resurrection?

11. Will only the soul be resurrected, or will the body be resurrected as well? Will only the Believers be resurrected?

12. What are the two categories of Resurrection? Who will be included in each?

13. What are the three types of *taaghoot*? Give examples of each.

14. What are the three ways in which we can disbelieve in the *taaghoot*? What are their rulings?

15. What are the five heads of the *taaghoot* listed by Sheikh Muhammad ibn 'Abdul Wahaab?

[/]

THALATHATUL-USUL
FINAL EXAM

STUDENT NAME:

This is a closed book exam. Use of notes is not permitted. Please answer each question as completely as possible. Write neatly and clearly, insh'Allaah. There is not enough room after each question to answer that question on the sheet. Use additional notebook paper for your answers, being sure to write your name on and number each page in order, insh'Allaah. I encourage you to write the Arabic for terms whenever you are able!

Definitions: Be sure to give their religious meaning. If you know their meaning in the language, then write it also, for extra points:

العقيدة:

التوحيد:

الإيمان:

العلم:

العبادة: (both the general and specific meanings)

أصل:

آية:

النية:

[/]

التوكل:

الدعاء:

الخوف:

الإسلام:

الأركان:

البدعة:

شرط/ شروط:

القدر:

الإحسان:

المعراج:

[/]

الإسراء:

الهجرة:

الغيب:

Short Answer:

1. Who is the author of *"Thalaathatul-Usool?* Give a brief biography of him. What are some lessons we can learn from his example?

2. What is the difference between *fard 'ayn* and *fard kfiyyah*? Give an example of each. What is the ruling on seeking knowledge?

3. Explain the position of knowledge in relation to speech and action.

4. What are the two types of *du'a*? Explain them and give an example of each.

5. Explain the difference between textual proof and intellectual proof? Which one is taken first and foremost in matters of the religion?

[/]

What is الشرك *ash-shirk*? For extra points, list the different types of *shirk* and give an example of each.

6. What is the most important thing that a Muslim must focus on in order to be successful in this life and the next? Why must he avoid being drawn too deeply into side issues?

7. Sheikh Muhammad ibn 'Abdul Wahaab, may Allaah have mercy upon him, states that it is obligatory upon every Muslim to *"...have knowledge of his Lord, his religion, and his Prophet, Muhammad, may Allaah's praise and salutations be upon him."* How are these three things foundations (*usool*) upon which the religion is built?

What is the meaning of the saying, "There is no power (to change) nor strength except with Allaah"- *la hawla wa la quwatta ila billaah*- (لا حول ولا قوة إلا بالله)? How does it relate to appealing to Allaah for assistance (*al-isti'aanah*)?

8.

9. What are the two categories of *ayaat,* by which we can learn about Allaah? Briefly explain them.

10. What are the two categories of Allaah's commands? Briefly describe them.

11. Give an example of worship in speech, worship in action, worship which is an act of the heart, worship which is hidden, and worship which is apparent.

12. What are the conditions by which it is permissible to seek something from other than Allaah?

13. What are the three categories of fear (*al-khawf*)? Briefly explain each one, with examples.

[/]

14. Explain the difference in the meaning of the words Islaam and *eemaan* when they are used separately and together.

15. Why must we obey both Allaah and the Messenger of Allaah, may Allaah's praise and salutations be upon him?

16. How does submission include the actions of the heart, tongue, and limbs?

17. What are the two categories of innovation? Give examples of each. . For extra credit, list the different classifications of the second type of innovation.

18. What are some of the fruits of the prayer? How can establishing the prayer, being consistent in it, and striving to perfect it assist us in our everyday life?

[/]

19. Allaah has pre-decreed all things. Does this mean that we don't have to strive to please Him, or do all that we can to avoid displeasing Him, since our reward or punishment has already been written? Are we not responsible for our actions because Allaah has decreed that we do them?

20. What are the four matters encompassed in belief in Allaah?

21. What is the definition of *at-taaghoot*? What are its heads, according to Sheikh Muhammad ibn 'Abdul Wahaab in this book?

22. Who was the Prophet Muhammad, may Allaah's praise and salutations be upon him? Include his name, lineage, where he was born, where he died, at what age he received prophethood, how long his prophethood extended and at what age he died. What made him a prophet? What made him a messenger? Briefly, what was his message?

[/]

23. What are the two main categories of *hijrah*? Why is one considered to be the foundation of the other?

24. What is the ruling on making *hijrah* from the land of disbelief to the land of Islaam, and what conditions are placed upon that?

25. What is the resurrection? Write the Arabic word as well as the definition.

26. What is the reckoning? Write the Arabic word as well as the definition.

27. What are the three ways in which we can disbelieve in the *taaghoot*? What are their rulings?

28. Why is it important that we know about the Messenger of Allaah, may Allaah's praise and salutations be upon him?

Multiple Choice:

1. Which of the following in NOT from the legislated categories of patience?

    a. Patience upon obedience to Allaah

    b. Patience in times of affluence and ease

    c. Patience upon not committing sins against Allaah

    d. Patience in times of adversity or affliction

2. Which of these is NOT one of the four characteristics mentioned that bring success to the people?

    a. Kindness and mercy towards the people

    b. True faith

    c. Enjoining one another upon good

    d. Righteous action

3. What is the greatest category of *tarbiyyah* which Allaah bestowed upon mankind?

    a. Raising and educating children

    b. Feeding and taking care of our families

    c. Allaah sending the messengers to guide us to that which is pleasing to Him

    d. Allaah sending the Books for us to read and interpret

4. What two things must be combined in *at-tawakkul* for it to be correct?

    a. One must make *du'a*

    b. Turning the matter entirely over to Allaah, the Mighty and Majestic

    c. One must not look for the reason for something occurring afterwards

    d. Repenting to Allaah for all of our sins

5. What aspect of *at-tawheed* does the Sheikh's saying, *He is the One whom I worship, and there is none other whom I worship other than Him* directly refer to?

    a. tawheed al-uloohiyyah

    b. tawheed ar-ruboobiyyah

    c. tawheed of Allaah's names and attributes

    d. tawheed of intention and desire

6. Which of the following is NOT included in testifying that Muhammad is the Messenger of Allaah?

    a. Affirmation of that which he narrates concerning the Hereafter, Paradise, the Fire, and other than them

    b. To worship Allaah only with that which He has legislated, and to not invent or introduce into the religion that which Allaah has not legislated.

    c. To leave off that which he has prohibited and spoken against, such as fornication, interest, and other than that from which Allaah and His Messenger have forbidden.

    d. To affirm that he did not die, and will return to earth on judgment day

7. Which of the following is NOT from the fruits of belief in the angels?

    a. Knowledge of the greatness of Allaah, the Most High, His Power, His authority and dominion.

    b. Worshipping the angels, as they were made of light and they worship Allaah much better than we do.

    c. Love of the angels for their worship of Allaah, the Most High.

    d. Thankfulness to Allaah, the Most High, for His care and concern from the welfare of mankind.

8. Which of the following are from the wisdom and benefits of the fast?

    a. One can increase in *taqwa* through it (fear of Allaah, and piety)

    b. One leaves behind his desires for Allaah

    c. One can stay up late at night spending time with friends and family

    d. It teaches one patience and gratitude

9. What are the three categories of *at-taghoot*?

    a. taaghoot of worship

    b. taaghoot of Allaah's names and attributes

    c. taaghoot of following

    d. taaghoot of obedience

10. Which of the following is not from the five stages of the Prophet's *da'wah*?

    a. calling to his tribe and those close to him

    b. prophethood

    c. messengership

    d. calling and warning those to whom he was sent

[/]

Life Application Questions

1. What are five ways we can show *al-baraa'* from the disbelievers? What are five ways we can show *al-walaa'* to the believers?

2. Allaah has created us to worship Him. What are some ways that you can strive worship Him with your heart, tongue and limbs, making your whole life directed towards pleasing Him?

3. Is it permissible to blindly follow in the religion? Explain. How does this affect how you would give *da'wah*?

4. You are now responsible for the knowledge gained in this course. List three things that you, personally, feel are the most important things that have learned, and which you wish to implement in your life, NOW?

[/]

5. What place should Islaam take in your life? How can you strive to make this a reality for YOU?

Extra Credit:

1. What are four ways in which some people go astray concerning Allaah's names and attributes? Give an example of each.

2. Write the Arabic and English words for each of the conditions of the *shahaadah*.

[/]

3. What order will events take place in, on the Day of Resurrection?

Any beneficial comments or suggestions concerning your experience with taking this course: (this does not count toward your grade)

[/]

(Extra page to be used whenever additional space is needed, please indicate lesson & question number)

(Extra page to be used whenever additional space is needed, please indicate lesson & question number)

[/]

(Extra page to be used whenever additional space is needed, please indicate lesson & question number)

Made in the USA
Middletown, DE
02 November 2014